THIS BOOK
BELONGS TO:

_____

A Journal From the Heart

President and Publisher: Jeramy Lanigan Landauer
Editor: Becky Johnston
Art Director: Lyne Neymeyer
Graphic Designer: Nicole Bratt
Prepress: Event Graphics
Printed in U.S.A.

Art Copyright © 1996 by P. Buckley Moss
Text Copyright © 1996 by Landauer Books, a division of
    Landauer Corporation,
    12251 Maffitt Road,
    Cumming, Iowa 50061

All rights reserved. No part of this book may be reproduced or
transmitted in any form or by any means, electronic or
mechanical, including photocopying, recording, or by any
information storage and retrieval system without permission in
writing from the publisher.

This book is printed on acid-free paper.

ISBN: 0964-6870-4-6

10 9 8 7 6 5 4 3 2 1
First Edition

Cover Image: *Apple Blossom Love*

A JOURNAL
FROM THE HEART

P. Buckley Moss ®

LANDAUER BOOKS
LANDAUER CORPORATION
CUMMING, IOWA

The Art of P. Buckley Moss

The Artist and Her Work

P. Buckley Moss, one of America's most
celebrated artists, is a phenomenon: in
her gifts and imagery, her popularity, and
in her ability to communicate on many
levels to many people.

P. Buckley Moss is also well-known
for her work with special education
groups and her generous donations to
charity. Primarily because of her dyslexia
and childhood struggles, Pat Moss has
become a role model to the learning
impaired and has raised millions of dollars
for children's charities.

Assisting her in these efforts is the
P. Buckley Moss Society with 60 chapters
and more than 20,000 members.

The P. Buckley Moss Museum

is located in the heart of the Shenandoah
Valley in Waynesboro, Virginia. Closely
resembling many of the larger houses built
by early 19th century settlers, it is an
appropriate setting for exhibiting works
by P. Buckley Moss, one of America's
most recognized and most popular artists.

Since the early 1960's, Moss has found
her inspiration and much of her subject
matter in Valley scenery and in the Amish

and Mennonite peoples of the area. She considers the example of the lifestyles of these traditional "Plain People" to hold an important message for modern society.

The Museum exhibits Moss' work and puts the talent of P. Buckley Moss in greater perspective—enabling the public to share more fully in her exhilarating vision.

The Featured Images are all offset lithographic reproductions, printed in limited editions:

Apple Blossom Love	American Apples
Christmas Carol	Autumn Ride
All Dressed Up	Winter at Yates Cider Mill
Stars of Love	Mother's Day
Tullie Smith House	Tender Shepherd
Black Sheep	Give Thanks*
Five Lambs	First Picnic
Our Teacher	Summer's Blessing
Shenandoah Memories	Golden Autumn
Never Ending Love	Love in Bloom
Born of Love	

All verse by Malcolm Henderson except as noted.

For further information regarding P. Buckley Moss limited edition prints and original paintings, and for the name of the authorized dealer nearest you, please call The Moss Portfolio at 800/430-1320.

Love Warms in Winter

Singing carols on Christmas Day
Away from home and traveling far,
Reminds us of the Wisemen,
Kings, and Shepherds, too
Lead us to Him, our shining star.

Christmas Carol, IS: 8" x 8", 1983

Love Blossoms in Spring

Quilted love so warm and true,

reflection of my love for you!

Stars of Love, IS: 12¾" x 11⁷⁄₁₆", 1993

Love Celebrates in Summer

Beautiful friend with your gentle face,
beside me always be.
Each of us has our rightful place,
and yours is next to me.

Black Sheep, IS: 17⁷⁄₁₆" x 12¾", 1983

Love Mellows in Autumn

A B C D E F G H I J K L M
N O P Q R S T U V W X Y Z

Throughout our lives, we hold in deep regard

Those who've helped us to succeed.

And, how often it seems to be,

Our teacher is the one who cared and shared—

but most of all believed.

Our Teacher, IS: 12⅛" x 12³⁄₁₆", 1992

Love Warms in Winter

First to last each other treasure,

Sharing always,

Love's full measure.

Never Ending Love, IS: 8" x 9⅛", 1995

Love Blossoms in Spring

Thank you, Mother,
for what we are:
Born of love, 'neath a lucky star!

Born of Love, IS: 7¼" x 9⅜", 1994

Love Celebrates in Summer

Hurray for the Fourth of July!
Wave the flag and celebrate with us—
Homegrown kids and apples for pie.

American Apples, IS: 11¼" x 8½", 1995

Love Mellows in Autumn

When granddad takes a trip to town
We come along for lots of fun,
Hoping for fresh cider and other apple treats
Before the day is done.

Autumn Ride, IS: 14¾" x 12", 1982

Love Warms in Winter

May our lives be filled
With such simple pleasures,
As watching children at their play.

Winter at Yates Cider Mill, IS: 9³⁄₁₆" x 10⅞", 1992

Love Blossoms in Spring

On this special day remember
I am part of you;
and when you add the total sum,
I love you through and through.

Love Celebrates in Summer

All the way my shepherd leads me,
Where He guides me I will stay.
For by His grace and tender care
I'm safely kept by night and day.

Tender Shepherd, IS: 9½" x 9½", 1983

Love Mellows in Autumn

For health and food,
For love and friends,
For everything Thy goodness sends...
We thank Thee.

Ralph Waldo Emerson

Give Thanks, IS: 9" x 9", 1993

Love Warms in Winter

When summer's pond is fully cloaked
by its frozen mantle;
Winter's play brings joy for all
As lovers dance in lover's arms.

Shenandoah Memories, IS: 16⅛" x 17⅜", 1993

Love Blossoms in Spring

May our memories always be,
Of this our special place;
Where love exchanged its first embrace!

First Picnic, IS: 12½" x 12¾", 1985

Love Celebrates in Summer

For God's grace let us pray
That deserving we may always be,
Of our precious little one;
Born to us this summer day.

Summer's Blessing, IS: 7¾" x 8¾", 1985

Love Mellows in Autumn

Please, God, just as we treasure the golden moments
At the close of the day,
Let us rejoice in the richest season of our lives—
when love mellows in Autumn.

Golden Autumn, IS: 17" x 17½", 1983

Love Warms in Winter

Love expressed with your permission,
Free of any inhibition.
Mistletoe, thank you well;
What may happen, who can tell?

Under the Mistletoe, IS: 8¼" x 8½", 1995

Love Blossoms in Spring

Sunshine and showers
Give us fragrant flowers,
With our spirits just as free,
We'll share the joys
Of all that springtime
Offers you and me.

Love in Bloom, IS: 11¼" x 11⅞", 1995

Warms in Winter Love Blooms in Spring Love Celebrates in Summer Love M
mer Love Mellows in Autumn Love Warms in Winter Love Blooms in Spring
oms in Spring Love Celebrates in Summer Love Mellows in Autumn Love War
umn Love Warms in Winter Love Blooms in Spring Love Celebrates in Summe
brates in Summer Love Mellows in Autumn Love Warms in Winter Love Blo
ter Love Blooms in Spring Love Celebrates in Summer Love Mellows in Autu
lows in Autumn Love Warms in Winter Love Blooms in Spring Love Celebra
Celebrates in Summer Love Mellows in Autumn Love Warms in Winter Love
Winter Love Blooms in Spring Love Celebrates in Summer Love Mellows in A
lows in Autumn Love Warms in Winter Love Blooms in Spring Love Celebra
Celebrates in Summer Love Mellows in Autumn Love Warms in Winter Love
Winter Love Blooms in Spring Love Celebrates in Summer Love Mellows in A
lows in Autumn Love Warms in Winter Love Blooms in Spring Love Celebra
Celebrates in Summer Love Mellows in Autumn Love Warms in Winter Love
Winter Love Blooms in Spring Love Celebrates in Summer Love Mellows in A
lows in Autumn Love Warms in Winter Love Blooms in Spring Love Celebra
Celebrates in Summer Love Mellows in Autumn Love Warms in Winter Love
Winter Love Blooms in Spring Love Celebrates in Summer Love Mellows in A
lows in Autumn Love Warms in Winter Love Blooms in Spring Love Celebra